The Jigaree

by Joy Cowley

I can see
a jigaree.
It is jumping after me.

Jumping here,
jumping there,
jigarees jump everywhere.

3

I can see
a jigaree.
It is dancing after me.

Dancing here,
dancing there,
jigarees dance everywhere.

I can see
a jigaree.
It is swimming after me.

Swimming here,
swimming there,
jigarees swim everywhere.

I can see
a jigaree.
It is riding after me.

**Riding here,
riding there,
jigarees ride everywhere.**

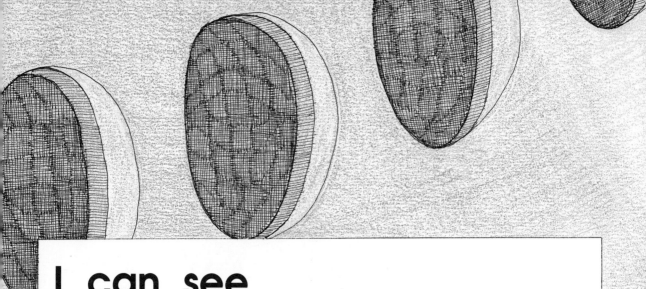

I can see
a jigaree.
It is skating after me.

Skating here,
skating there,
jigarees skate everywhere.

I can see
a jigaree.
It is climbing after me.

Climbing here,
climbing there,
jigarees climb everywhere.

I can see
a jigaree.
It is flying after me.

Flying here,
flying there,
jigarees fly everywhere.

14

Jigaree, jigaree,
I will take you...

home with me.